Songs of Prayer

Sixteen favourite sacred solos
arranged by
Alan Ridout & Anthea Smith

Kevin
Mayhew

Front Cover: *The Virgin in Prayer* by Sassoferrato (1609-1685).
Reproduced by courtesy of the Trustees, The National Gallery, London.

Cover designed by Juliette Clarke and Graham Johnstone
Picture Research: Jane Rayson

First published in Great Britain in 1994 by Kevin Mayhew Ltd

ISBN 0 86209 484 4
Catalogue No: 1450008

All or part of these pieces have been arranged by Alan Ridout and
Anthea Smith and are the copyright of Kevin Mayhew Ltd.

Music Editor: Anthea Smith
Music Setting: Tricia Oliver

Printed and bound in Great Britain

Contents

Foreword

As its title suggests, this book is a collection of many of the best-loved sacred solos. The voice part is intended primarily for sopranos or tenors, but many of the settings lie in the middle range of these voices and can equally well be sung by altos or basses.

The accompaniments are for the organ, using the manual and pedal indications as suggested. However, the music has been arranged so that, with one or two minor adjustments, it may be played on the piano or any keyboard.

PIE JESU

Text: From the Requiem Mass
Music: Gabriel Fauré (1845 - 1924)

5

re - qui - em, sem - pi - ter - nam re - qui - em.

Pi - e, pi - e Je - su, pi - e Je - su Do - mi - ne,

do - na e - is, do - na e - is sem - pi - ter - nam

re - qui - em, sem - pi - ter - nam re - qui - em.

7

GOD BE IN MY HEAD

Text: from the *Sarum Primer* (1514)
Music: Henry Walford Davies (1869 - 1941)

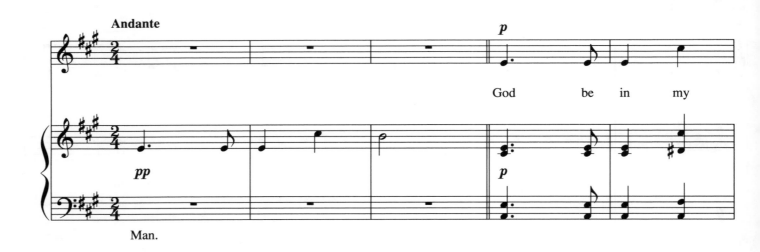

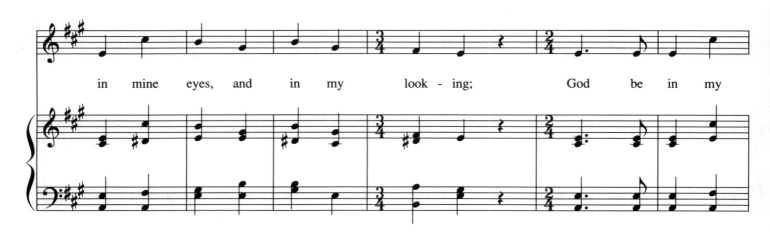

mouth, and in my speak - ing; God be in my

heart, and in my think - ing; God be

at mine end, and at my de - part - ing.

JESU, JOY OF MAN'S DESIRING

Text: Robert Bridges (1844 - 1930)
Music: Johann Sebastian Bach (1685 - 1750)

bright,
rings,

drawn   by
where   the

espress.

thee,   our   souls   as –   pir – ing,
flock,   in   thee   con – fid – ing,

soar   to   un – cre – a – ted   light.
drink   of   joy   from   death – less   springs.

Word of God, our
Theirs is beau - ty's

flesh that fa - shioned
fair - est plea - sure:

with the fire of
theirs is wis - dom's

life im - pas - sioned
ho - liest trea - sure:

striv - ing still to
thou dost e - ver

truth un - known,
lead thine own

soar - ing, dy - ing, round thy throne.
in the love of joys un - known.

AVE VERUM CORPUS

Text: 14th century
Music: Wolfgang Amadeus Mozart (1756 - 1791)

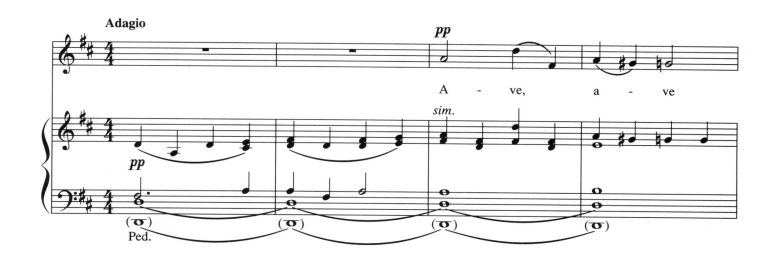

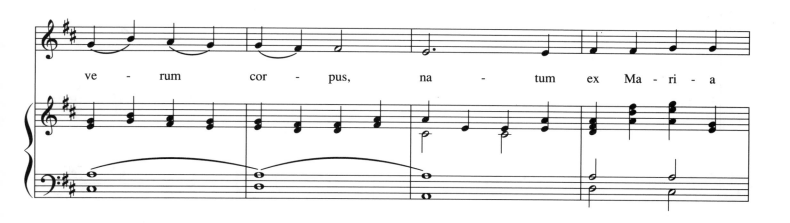

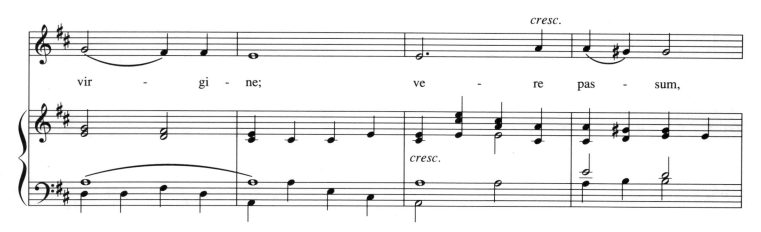

im - mo - la - tum in cru - ce pro

ho - mi - ne.

Cu - jus la - tus per - fo -

Man.

ra - tum un - da flux - it et san - gui -

16

ne;   es - to no - bis prae - gu -

sta - tum in mor - - tis ex - a - mi - ne, in

mor - - - - tis ex -

a - mi - ne.

Ped.

17

PANIS ANGELICUS

Text: Thomas Aquinas (1227 - 1274)
Music: César Franck (1822 - 1890)

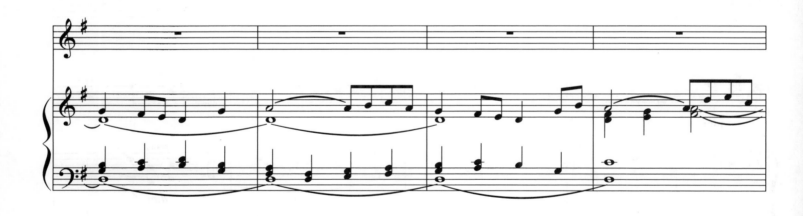

Pa - nis an - ge - li -cus fit pa - nis ho - mi -num,

dat pa - nis coe - li -cus fi - gu - ris ter - mi - num:

O res mi - ra - bi -lis: man - du - cat Do - mi -num

pau - per, pau - per, ser - vus et hu - mi - lis,

pau - per, pau - per, ser - vus et hu - mi - lis.

Man.

Pa - nis an - ge - li - cus fit pa - nis ho - mi - num,

Ped.

dat pa - nis coe - li - cus fi - gu - ris ter - mi - num:

O res mi - ra - bi -lis: man - du - cat Do - mi -num

pau - per, pau - per, ser - vus et hu - mi - lis,

cresc.

ff

dim.

pau - per, pau - per, ser - vus, ser - vus et hu - mi -

f

dim.

lis.

rall.

mp

Man.

21

AVE MARIA

Text: Luke 1
Music: adapted from J. S. Bach
by Charles Gounod (1818 - 1893)

gra - ti - a ple - na, Do - mi - nus te - cum, be - ne - di - cta tu in mu - li - e - ri - bus, et be - ne - di - ctus fru - ctus

ven - tris tu - i Je - sus.

cresc. poco a poco

San - cta Ma - ri - a, san - cta Ma -

cresc. poco a poco

ri - a, Ma - ri - a! O - ra pro

cresc.

no - bis, no - bis pec - ca - to - ri - bus

nunc et in ho - ra, in ho - ra

mor - tis no - strae, A - men,

A - men.

BIST DU BEI MIR

Text: Michael Forster (*b.* 1946)
Music: Johann Sebastian Bach (1685 - 1750)

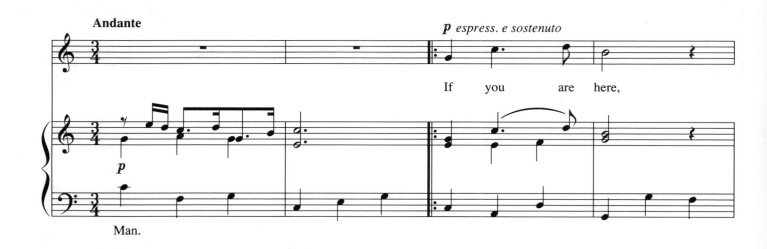

with what con - tent - ment I'll find in death my life's re -
pose, I'll find in death my life's re - pose. O sweet in -
deed would be my end - ing, if you, in
death my soul be - friend - ing, with gen - tle hands my eye - lids close.

O sweet in - deed would be my end - ing, if you, in
death my soul be - friend - ing, with gen - tle hands my eye - lids close.
If you are here, with what con - tent - ment
I'll find in death my life's re - pose, I'll find in death my life's re - pose.

28

O FOR THE WINGS OF A DOVE

Text: Psalm 55: 6, 7
Music: Felix Mendelssohn (1809 - 1847)

O for the wings, for the wings of a dove! Far a - way, far a -

way would I rove. O for the wings, for the wings of a dove!

Far a - way, far a - way, far a - way, far a - way would I rove. In the

wil - der - ness build me a nest, and re - main there for e - ver at

rest, in the wil - der - ness build me, build me a nest,

and re - main there for e - ver at rest, in the wil - der - ness

build me a nest, and re - main there for e - ver at rest.

And re - main there for e - ver at rest, and re - main there for

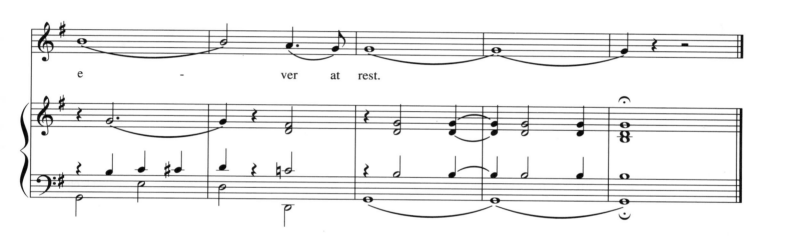

e - ver at rest.

BROTHER JAMES' AIR

Text: Psalm 23 from *The Scottish Psalter* (1650)
Music: James Leith MacBeth Bain (c.1860 - 1925)

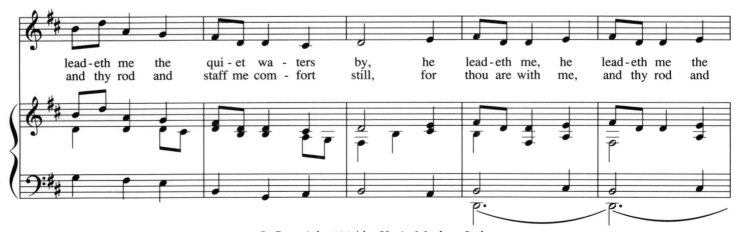

5. Good -

Man.

ness and mer - cy all my life shall sure - ly fol - low me, and

Ped.

in God's house for e - ver - more my dwell - ing place shall be, and

rall.

in God's house for e - ver - more my dwell - ing place shall be.

rall.

AVE VERUM CORPUS

Text: 14th century
Music: Edward Elgar (1857 - 1934)

ri - a vir - gi - ne; ve - re pas - sum, im - mo - la - tum in cru -

ce pro ho - mi - ne. Cu - jus la - tus per - fo - ra - tum ve - ro

cresc.

Man.

flu - xit san - gui - ne; e - sto no - bis prae - gu - sta - tum, mor - tis

in ex - a - mi - ne. Cu - jus la - tus per - fo - ra - tum ve - ro

Ped.

36

flu - xit san - gui - ne; e - sto no - bis prae - gu - sta - tum, mor - tis in ex - a - mi - ne. O cle - mens, O pi - e, O dul - cis Je - su, fi - li Ma - ri - ae.

O REST IN THE LORD

Text: Psalm 37
Music: Felix Mendelssohn (1809 - 1847)

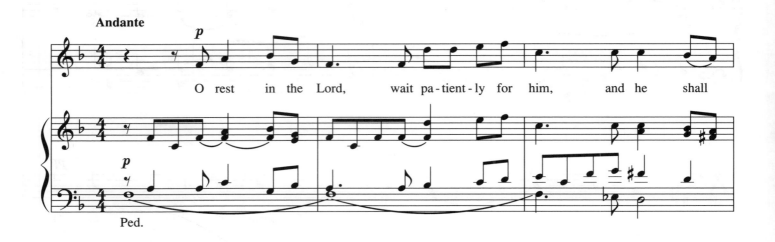

O rest in the Lord, wait pa-tient-ly for him, and he shall

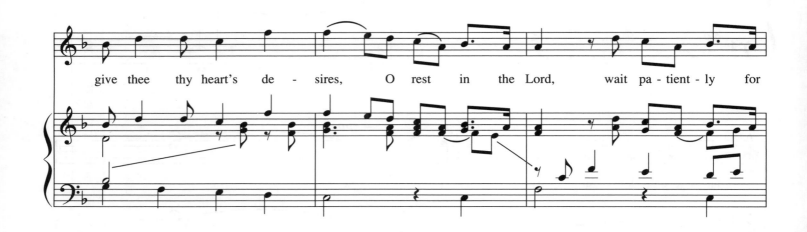

give thee thy heart's de - sires, O rest in the Lord, wait pa-tient-ly for

him, and he shall give thee thy heart's de - sires, and he shall

give thee thy heart's de - sires. Com - mit thy way un - to him, and trust in

Man.

him, com - mit thy way un - to him, and trust in him, and fret not thy -

Ped.

self be - cause of e - vil do - ers. O rest in the Lord, wait pa - tient - ly for

him, wait pa - tient - ly for him, O rest in the Lord, wait pa - tient - ly for

him, and he shall give thee thy heart's de - sires, and he shall

give thee thy heart's de - sires, and he shall give thee thy heart's de -

sires. O rest in the Lord, O rest in the Lord, and wait,

wait pa - tient - ly for him.

THE VIRGIN'S SLUMBER SONG

Text: Michael Forster (*b.* 1946)
Music: Max Reger (1873 - 1916)

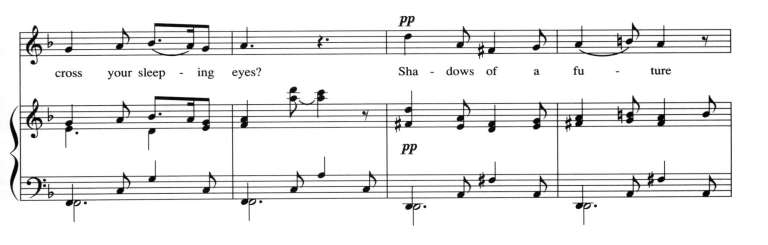

O child of pro - mise — such a cost, but such a prize!

O soft - ly slum - ber,

child of grace! Child of sor - row,

child of joy, child of my - ste - ry di - vine, may your peace - ful,

trust - ing sleep   be   of hope   the   seal   and sign.

O   soft - ly   slum   -   ber,

child   of   grace!

I KNOW THAT MY REDEEMER LIVETH

Text: Job 19:25

Music: George Frideric Handel (1685 - 1759)

and that he shall stand at the lat - ter day up - on the earth, I know that my Re -

up - on the earth,   up - on the

earth.

mf

LEAD ME, LORD

Text: Psalm 5:8; 4:8
Music: Samuel Sebastian Wesley (1810 - 1876)

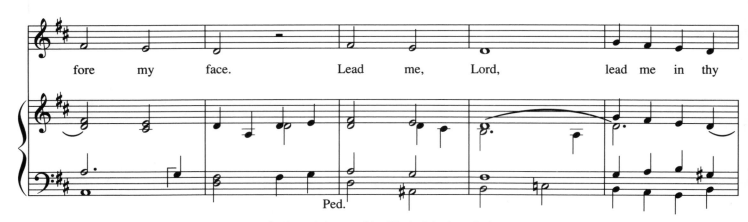

right - eous-ness, make thy way plain be - fore my face.

Man.

For it is thou, Lord, thou, Lord, on - ly, that mak - est me

dwell in safe - ty. For it is thou, Lord,

Ped.

thou, Lord, on - ly, that mak - est me dwell in safe - ty.

rit.

49

SHEEP MAY SAFELY GRAZE

Text: Michael Forster (*b.* 1946)
Music: Johann Sebastian Bach (1685 - 1750)

Sheep may safe - ly graze un - hin - dered with the faith - ful

shep - herd near.   Sheep may safe - ly graze un - hin - dered,

sheep   may   safe - ly   graze   un - hin - dered,

with   the   faith - ful   shep - herd near,   with   the

faith - ful shep - herd near.

(Man.)

51

2nd time only

2nd time only

Where the lea - ders of the na - tions seek the heal - ing

(Ped.)

of cre - a - tion, peace will put an end to fear.

(Man.)

52

53

AVE MARIA

Text: Luke 1
Music: Franz Schubert (1797 - 1828)

na,   Ma - ri - a gra-ti-a ple - na,   Do -mi - nus te-
bis,   o - ra, o - ra pro no - bis   pec -ca - to - ri-

cum,   be - ne - di - cta tu in mu - li - e - ri-bus,   et
bus,   nunc et in ho - ra mor - tis no - strae,   in

be - ne - di - ctus,   et be - ne - di - ctus fru - ctus
ho - ra mor - tis no - strae,   nunc et in ho - ra mor - tis

ven - tris,   ven - tris tu - i, Je - sus.
no - strae,   in ho - ra mor - tis no - strae.

A - ve Ma - ri - a!
A - ve Ma - ri - a!

dim. al fine